AGRA
UN DÍA

GRATEFUL one DAY AT A TiME

*a journal to cultivate small simple
moments of gratitude and self-care*

*un diario para cultivar pequeños y sencillos
momentos de gratitud y cuidado personal*

Published by:
A Peace of Werk Publications
In partnership with Eliza Todd Designs, LLC
Illustrations: Eliza Todd
Translation: Aleea Armijo, MA
This version in partnership with Knowing You Matter 501c3

Please visit: www.apeaceofwerk.com for more books, resources and free downloads.
If you are struggling or know someone who is, please visit: www.knowingyoumatter.org
There is help. There is hope.

a
peace of
werk
PUBLICATIONS

This Book Belongs to:
Este libro pertenece a:

_____

"We live in a world where joy and empathy and pleasure are all around us, there for the noticing."

-Ira Glass

"Vivimos en un mundo donde la alegría, la empatía y el placer están a nuestro alrededor, ahí para que nos demos cuenta."

-Ira Glass

INTRODUCTION

Life is a compilation of rich simple moments
woven together to create the tapestry of a story. Being able to
find meaning, hope and gratitude in the mundane and
painful bits empowers us to create greater well-being. This
is the ultimate form of self-care; to choose to employ the
power of choice and focus on the authentically good that
exists even in the uncertain times of life. It is the small
choices that create great impact within us and within
the world around us.

Scientific research shows that taking even a few minutes
regularly to reflect on some things in our life with gratitude
will result in greater happiness and calmed anxiety. In
addition there is evidence that writing down your worries
helps to get them off your mind and free you up to find
a bit more calm and peace. This book is meant to provide
you a small space to develop a manageable practice that
won't require a lot of time but hopefully provides you the start
to building a habit that serves you for years to come.

"Gratitude makes sense of the past, brings peace for today, and creates a vision for tomorrow." -Melody Beattie

__/__/___ Today I am grateful for/Hoy estoy agradecido por:

_____

_____

_____

__/__/___ Today I am grateful for:

_____

_____

_____

__/__/___ Today I am grateful for:

_____

_____

_____

__/__/___ Today I am grateful for:

_____

_____

_____

__/__/___ Today I am grateful for:

_____

_____

_____

Kindness takes Courage

"La gratitud le da sentido al pasado, trae paz para hoy y crea una visión para el futuro." -Melody Beattie

___/___/___ Today I am grateful for:

_____

_____

_____

___/___/___ Today I am grateful for:

_____

_____

_____

Self-care I practiced this week / Cuidado personal que apliqué esta semana:

_____

_____

_____

_____

_____

One thing I am looking forward to / Una cosa que me emociona:

_____

_____

Leave any worries here / Deja cualquier preocupación aquí:

_____

_____

_____

La amabilidad requiere valor

___/___/___ Today I am grateful for / Hoy estoy agradecido por:

_____

_____

_____

___/___/___ Today I am grateful for:

_____

_____

_____

___/___/___ Today I am grateful for:

_____

_____

_____

___/___/___ Today I am grateful for:

_____

_____

_____

___/___/___ Today I am grateful for:

_____

_____

_____

Kindness takes Courage

> *"Tómese el tiempo para ver los milagros silenciosos que no son tan obvios de notar."*
> -John O'Donohue

__/ /__ Today I am grateful for:

_____

_____

_____

__/ /__ Today I am grateful for:

_____

_____

_____

Self-care I practiced this week / Cuidado personal que apliqué esta semana:

_____

_____

_____

_____

_____

One thing I am looking forward to / Una cosa que me emociona:

_____

_____

Leave any worries here / Deja cualquier preocupación aquí:

_____

_____

_____

La amabilidad requiere valor

● ●

"Hem your blessings with thankfulness so they don't unravel." -Unknown

___/___/___ Today I am grateful for/Hoy estoy agradecido por:

_____

_____

_____

___/___/___ Today I am grateful for:

_____

_____

_____

___/___/___ Today I am grateful for:

_____

_____

_____

___/___/___ Today I am grateful for:

_____

_____

_____

___/___/___ Today I am grateful for:

_____

_____

_____

Kindness takes Courage

"Dobla tus bendiciones con agradecimiento para que no se deshagan." -Desconocido

_/_/_ Today I am grateful for:

_____
_____
_____

_/_/_ Today I am grateful for:

_____
_____
_____

Self-care I practiced this week / Cuidado personal que apliqué esta semana:

_____
_____
_____
_____
_____

One thing I am looking forward to / Una cosa que me emociona:

_____
_____

Leave any worries here / Deja cualquier preocupación aquí:

_____
_____
_____

La amabilidad requiere valor

• • • •• • • •• • • • • • • • •• • •• • • • •• • • • • •• • • • • • •• • •

"To walk in nature is to witness a thousand miracles." -Mary Davis

___/___/___ Today I am grateful for / Hoy estoy agradecido por:

_____

_____

_____

___/___/___ Today I am grateful for:

_____

_____

_____

___/___/___ Today I am grateful for:

_____

_____

_____

___/___/___ Today I am grateful for:

_____

_____

_____

___/___/___ Today I am grateful for:

_____

_____

_____

Kindness takes Courage

"Caminar en la naturaleza es presenciar mil milagros." -Mary Davis

___/___/___ Today I am grateful for:

_____

_____

_____

___/___/___ Today I am grateful for:

_____

_____

_____

Self-care I practiced this week / Cuidado personal que apliqué esta semana:

_____

_____

_____

_____

_____

One thing I am looking forward to / Una cosa que me emociona:

_____

_____

Leave any worries here / Deja cualquier preocupación aquí:

_____

_____

_____

La amabilidad requiere valor

Your worth is not measured by your productivity

Tu valor no está definido por tu productividad

Mistakes Are Proof you Are trying

LOS ERRORES SON UNA PRUEBA DE QUE LO ESTÁS INTENTANDO

"Be faithful in the small things because it is in them that your strength lies." –Mother Teresa

___/___/___ Today I am grateful for/Hoy estoy agradecido por:

_____

_____

_____

___/___/___ Today I am grateful for:

_____

_____

_____

___/___/___ Today I am grateful for:

_____

_____

_____

___/___/___ Today I am grateful for:

_____

_____

_____

___/___/___ Today I am grateful for:

_____

_____

_____

Kindness takes Courage

"Sé fiel en las cosas pequeñas porque en ellas reside tu fuerza." -Mother Teresa

__/__/___   Today I am grateful for:

_____

_____

_____

__/__/___   Today I am grateful for:

_____

_____

_____

Self-care I practiced this week/Cuidado personal que apliqué esta semana:

_____

_____

_____

_____

_____

One thing I am looking forward to / Una cosa que me emociona:

_____

_____

Leave any worries here / Deja cualquier preocupación aquí:

_____

_____

_____

La amabilidad requiere valor

"Gratitude is when memory is stored in the heart and not the mind." -Lionel Hampton

___/___/___ Today I am grateful for/Hoy estoy agradecido por:

_____

_____

_____

_____

___/___/___ Today I am grateful for:

_____

_____

_____

_____

___/___/___ Today I am grateful for:

_____

_____

_____

_____

___/___/___ Today I am grateful for:

_____

_____

_____

_____

___/___/___ Today I am grateful for:

_____

_____

_____

_____

Kindness takes Courage

"La gratitud es cuando la memoria se guarda en el corazón y no en la mente." -Lionel Hampton

___/___/___ Today I am grateful for:

_____

_____

_____

___/___/___ Today I am grateful for:

_____

_____

_____

Self-care I practiced this week / Cuidado personal que apliqué esta semana:

_____

_____

_____

_____

_____

One thing I am looking forward to / Una cosa que me emociona:

_____

_____

Leave any worries here / Deja cualquier preocupación aquí:

_____

_____

_____

La amabilidad requiere valor

• •

"When you arise in the morning, think of what a precious privilege it is to be alive-to breathe, to think, to enjoy, to love." -Marcus Aurelius

___/___/___ Today I am grateful for/Hoy estoy agradecido por:

_____

_____

_____

___/___/___ Today I am grateful for:

_____

_____

_____

___/___/___ Today I am grateful for:

_____

_____

_____

___/___/___ Today I am grateful for:

_____

_____

_____

___/___/___ Today I am grateful for:

_____

_____

_____

Kindness takes Courage

"Cuando te levantes por la mañana, piensa en el precioso privilegio que es estar vivo, respirar, pensar, disfrutar, amar." -Marcus Aurelius

___/___/___ Today I am grateful for:

_____

_____

_____

___/___/___ Today I am grateful for:

_____

_____

_____

Self-care I practiced this week / Cuidado personal que apliqué esta semana:

_____

_____

_____

_____

_____

One thing I am looking forward to / Una cosa que me emociona:

_____

_____

Leave any worries here / Deja cualquier preocupación aquí:

_____

_____

_____

La amabilidad requiere valor

"There are two ways to live: you can live as if nothing is a miracle, or you can live as if everything is a miracle." -Albert Einstein

___/___/_____ Today I am grateful for/Hoy estoy agradecido por:

_____

_____

_____

___/___/_____ Today I am grateful for:

_____

_____

_____

___/___/_____ Today I am grateful for:

_____

_____

_____

___/___/_____ Today I am grateful for:

_____

_____

_____

___/___/_____ Today I am grateful for:

_____

_____

_____

Kindness takes Courage

"Hay dos maneras de vivir: puedes vivir como si nada fuera un milagro o puedes vivir como si todo fuera un milagro." -Albert Einstein

___/___/___ Today I am grateful for:

_____

_____

_____

___/___/___ Today I am grateful for:

_____

_____

_____

Self-care I practiced this week / Cuidado personal que apliqué esta semana:

_____

_____

_____

_____

_____

One thing I am looking forward to / Una cosa que me emociona:

_____

_____

Leave any worries here / Deja cualquier preocupación aquí:

_____

_____

_____

La amabilidad requiere valor

• • • •• • • • • • • • • • • •••• • • • •••• • • •• • • • • • • •

if You
Love
Someone
let
them
Know
(INCLUDING YOU)

Si amas a alguien házselo saber (incluYéndote)

FRIENDSHIP
ISN'T
A BIG
THING
IT'S A
MILLION
LITTLE
THINGS

"I have too many flaws to be perfect, but I have too many blessings to be ungrateful." -Unknown

__/__/____ Today I am grateful for/Hoy estoy agradecido por:

_____

_____

_____

__/__/____ Today I am grateful for:

_____

_____

_____

__/__/____ Today I am grateful for:

_____

_____

_____

__/__/____ Today I am grateful for:

_____

_____

_____

__/__/____ Today I am grateful for:

_____

_____

_____

Kindness takes Courage

"Tengo demasiados defectos para ser perfecto, pero tengo demasiadas bendiciones para ser un desagradecido." -Desconocido

___/___/___ Today I am grateful for:

_____

_____

_____

___/___/___ Today I am grateful for:

_____

_____

_____

Self-care I practiced this week / Cuidado personal que apliqué esta semana:

_____

_____

_____

_____

_____

One thing I am looking forward to / Una cosa que me emociona:

_____

_____

Leave any worries here / Deja cualquier preocupación aquí:

_____

_____

_____

La amabilidad requiere valor

• • • •• • • • • • • • • • •• • • • • • • • • • •• •

"Happiness cannot be traveled to, owned, earned, worn, or consumed. Happiness is the spiritual experience of living every minute with love, grace, and gratitude." -Denis Waitley

___/___/___ Today I am grateful for / Hoy estoy agradecido por:

_____

_____

_____

___/___/___ Today I am grateful for:

_____

_____

_____

___/___/___ Today I am grateful for:

_____

_____

_____

___/___/___ Today I am grateful for:

_____

_____

_____

___/___/___ Today I am grateful for:

_____

_____

_____

Kindness takes Courage

"La felicidad no se puede viajar, poseer, ganar, usar o consumir.
La felicidad es la experiencia espiritual de vivir cada minuto con amor,
gracia, y gratitud." -Denis Waitley

__/__/____ Today I am grateful for:

_____

_____

_____

__/__/____ Today I am grateful for:

_____

_____

_____

Self-care I practiced this week / Cuidado personal que apliqué esta semana:

_____

_____

_____

_____

_____

One thing I am looking forward to / Una cosa que me emociona:

_____

_____

Leave any worries here / Deja cualquier preocupación aquí:

_____

_____

_____

La amabilidad requiere valor

"It's no small thing to sit together and simply say,
I am glad you are here." -Brian Andreas

___/___/___ Today I am grateful for/Hoy estoy agradecido por:

_____

_____

_____

___/___/___ Today I am grateful for:

_____

_____

_____

___/___/___ Today I am grateful for:

_____

_____

_____

___/___/___ Today I am grateful for:

_____

_____

_____

___/___/___ Today I am grateful for:

_____

_____

_____

Kindness takes Courage
● ●● • ● ● • • ● • ● ● ● ● ● ● ●—● • ● ●● ●● ● • ● ● ● ● ● ● ● ●

No es poca cosa sentarse juntos y simplemente decir:
Me alegro de que estés aquí." –Brian Andreas

__/ /__ Today I am grateful for:

_____

_____

_____

__/ /__ Today I am grateful for:

_____

_____

_____

Self-care I practiced this week / Cuidado personal que apliqué esta semana:

_____

_____

_____

_____

_____

One thing I am looking forward to / Una cosa que me emociona:

_____

_____

Leave any worries here / Deja cualquier preocupación aquí:

_____

_____

_____

La amabilidad requiere valor

• •

"The more light you allow within you, the brighter the world you live in will be." -Shakti Gawain

___/___/___ Today I am grateful for/Hoy estoy agradecido por:

_____

_____

_____

___/___/___ Today I am grateful for:

_____

_____

_____

___/___/___ Today I am grateful for:

_____

_____

_____

___/___/___ Today I am grateful for:

_____

_____

_____

___/___/___ Today I am grateful for:

_____

_____

_____

Kindness takes Courage

*"Cuanta más luz permitas dentro de ti, más brillante
será el mundo en el que vives." -Shakti Gawain*

_/_/___   Today I am grateful for:

_____

_____

_____

_/_/___   Today I am grateful for:

_____

_____

_____

Self-care I practiced this week / Cuidado personal que apliqué esta semana:

_____

_____

_____

_____

_____

One thing I am looking forward to / Una cosa que me emociona:

_____

_____

Leave any worries here / Deja cualquier preocupación aquí:

_____

_____

_____

La amabilidad requiere valor

Rest
your mind
Calm
your heart
Free
your spirit

Descansa tu mente, calma tu corazón, libera tu espíritu

INHALA, EXHALA

"When gratitude becomes an essential foundation in our lives, miracles start to appear everywhere." -Emmanuel Dagher

___/___/___ Today I am grateful for/Hoy estoy agradecido por:

_____

_____

_____

___/___/___ Today I am grateful for:

_____

_____

_____

___/___/___ Today I am grateful for:

_____

_____

_____

___/___/___ Today I am grateful for:

_____

_____

_____

___/___/___ Today I am grateful for:

_____

_____

_____

Kindness takes Courage

"Cuando la gratitud se convierte en una base esencial en nuestras vidas, los milagros comienzan a aparecer en todas partes." -Emmanuel Dagher

__/__/__ Today I am grateful for:

_____

_____

_____

__/__/__ Today I am grateful for:

_____

_____

_____

Self-care I practiced this week / Cuidado personal que apliqué esta semana:

_____

_____

_____

_____

One thing I am looking forward to / Una cosa que me emociona:

_____

_____

Leave any worries here / Deja cualquier preocupación aquí:

_____

_____

_____

La amabilidad requiere valor

"The secret to having it all is knowing you already do." –Unknown

___/___/___ Today I am grateful for/Hoy estoy agradecido por:

_____

_____

_____

___/___/___ Today I am grateful for:

_____

_____

_____

___/___/___ Today I am grateful for:

_____

_____

_____

___/___/___ Today I am grateful for:

_____

_____

_____

___/___/___ Today I am grateful for:

_____

_____

_____

Kindness takes Courage

_/_/__ Today I am grateful for:

_____

_____

_____

_/_/__ Today I am grateful for:

_____

_____

_____

Self-care I practiced this week / Cuidado personal que apliqué esta semana:

_____

_____

_____

_____

_____

One thing I am looking forward to / Una cosa que me emociona:

_____

_____

Leave any worries here / Deja cualquier preocupación aquí:

_____

_____

_____

La amabilidad requiere valor

"This is a wonderful day. I've never seen this one before." -Maya Angelou

___/___/___ Today I am grateful for/Hoy estoy agradecido por:

_____

_____

_____

___/___/___ Today I am grateful for:

_____

_____

_____

___/___/___ Today I am grateful for:

_____

_____

_____

___/___/___ Today I am grateful for:

_____

_____

_____

___/___/___ Today I am grateful for:

_____

_____

_____

Kindness takes Courage

___/___/___ Today I am grateful for:

_____

_____

_____

___/___/___ Today I am grateful for:

_____

_____

_____

Self-care I practiced this week / Cuidado personal que apliqué esta semana:

_____

_____

_____

_____

_____

One thing I am looking forward to / Una cosa que me emociona:

_____

_____

Leave any worries here / Deja cualquier preocupación aquí:

_____

_____

_____

La amabilidad requiere valor

"Let us be grateful to people who make us happy." -Marcel Proust

___/___/___ Today I am grateful for/Hoy estoy agradecido por:

_____

_____

_____

___/___/___ Today I am grateful for:

_____

_____

_____

___/___/___ Today I am grateful for:

_____

_____

_____

___/___/___ Today I am grateful for:

_____

_____

_____

___/___/___ Today I am grateful for:

_____

_____

_____

Kindness takes Courage

___/___/___ Today I am grateful for:

_____

_____

_____

___/___/___ Today I am grateful for:

_____

_____

_____

Self-care I practiced this week / Cuidado personal que apliqué esta semana:

_____

_____

_____

_____

_____

One thing I am looking forward to / Una cosa que me emociona:

_____

_____

Leave any worries here / Deja cualquier preocupación aquí:

_____

_____

_____

La amabilidad requiere valor

"We must be willing to let go of the life we have planned, so as to accept the life that is waiting for us."

-Joseph Campbell

"Debemos estar dispuestos a dejar ir la vida que hemos planeado, para aceptar la vida que nos espera." -Joseph Campbell

think of some
things you
would like to
release and
write those
inside the
lanterns and
imagine them
floating away

Piensa en algunas
cosas que te gustaría
liberar y escríbelas
dentro de las linternas
e imagínalas flotando

let it
go

déjalo ir

"Enjoy the little things, for one day you may look back and realize they were big things." -Robert Brault

___/___/___ Today I am grateful for/Hoy estoy agradecido por:

_____

_____

_____

___/___/___ Today I am grateful for:

_____

_____

_____

___/___/___ Today I am grateful for:

_____

_____

_____

___/___/___ Today I am grateful for:

_____

_____

_____

___/___/___ Today I am grateful for:

_____

_____

_____

Kindness takes Courage

"Disfruta de las pequeñas cosas por un día, puedes mirar hacia atrás y darte cuenta de que eran cosas grandes." -Robert Brault

_/ _/____ Today I am grateful for:

_____

_____

_____

_/ _/____ Today I am grateful for:

_____

_____

_____

Self-care I practiced this week / Cuidado personal que apliqué esta semana:

_____

_____

_____

_____

_____

One thing I am looking forward to / Una cosa que me emociona:

_____

_____

Leave any worries here / Deja cualquier preocupación aquí:

_____

_____

_____

La amabilidad requiere valor

• •

___/___/___ Today I am grateful for/Hoy estoy agradecido por:

_____

_____

_____

___/___/___ Today I am grateful for:

_____

_____

_____

___/___/___ Today I am grateful for:

_____

_____

_____

___/___/___ Today I am grateful for:

_____

_____

_____

___/___/___ Today I am grateful for:

_____

_____

_____

Kindness takes Courage

___/___/___ Today I am grateful for:

_____

_____

_____

___/___/___ Today I am grateful for:

_____

_____

_____

Self-care I practiced this week/Cuidado personal que apliqué esta semana:

_____

_____

_____

_____

_____

One thing I am looking forward to / Una cosa que me emociona:

_____

_____

Leave any worries here / Deja cualquier preocupación aquí:

_____

_____

_____

La amabilidad requiere valor

"When eating fruit, remember the one who planted the tree."
-Vietnamese Proverb

___/___/___ Today I am grateful for/Hoy estoy agradecido por:

_____

_____

_____

___/___/___ Today I am grateful for:

_____

_____

_____

___/___/___ Today I am grateful for:

_____

_____

_____

___/___/___ Today I am grateful for:

_____

_____

_____

___/___/___ Today I am grateful for:

_____

_____

_____

Kindness takes Courage

"Al comer fruta, acuérdate del que plantó el árbol."
-Proverbio Vietnamita

___/___/___ Today I am grateful for:

_____

_____

_____

___/___/___ Today I am grateful for:

_____

_____

_____

Self-care I practiced this week / Cuidado personal que apliqué esta semana:

_____

_____

_____

_____

_____

One thing I am looking forward to / Una cosa que me emociona:

_____

_____

Leave any worries here / Deja cualquier preocupación aquí:

_____

_____

_____

La amabilidad requiere valor

"Don't let what you want keep you from appreciating what you have." -Eliza Todd

___/___/___ Today I am grateful for/Hoy estoy agradecido por:

_____

_____

_____

___/___/___ Today I am grateful for:

_____

_____

_____

___/___/___ Today I am grateful for:

_____

_____

_____

___/___/___ Today I am grateful for:

_____

_____

_____

___/___/___ Today I am grateful for:

_____

_____

_____

Kindness takes Courage

*"No dejes que lo que quieres te impida apreciar
lo que tienes." -Eliza Todd*

___/___/___ Today I am grateful for:

_____

_____

_____

___/___/___ Today I am grateful for:

_____

_____

_____

Self-care I practiced this week / Cuidado personal que apliqué esta semana:

_____

_____

_____

_____

_____

One thing I am looking forward to / Una cosa que me emociona:

_____

_____

Leave any worries here / Deja cualquier preocupación aquí:

_____

_____

_____

La amabilidad requiere valor

things
that
bring
me
joy

Fill the rays of sun with things that bring you joy

cosas
que
me
traen
algería

Llena los rayos del sol con cosas que te traigan alegría

"Gratitude can transform common days into thanksgivings, turn routine jobs into joy, and change ordinary opportunities into blessings." -William Arthur Ward

___/___/___ Today I am grateful for/Hoy estoy agradecido por:

_____

_____

_____

___/___/___ Today I am grateful for:

_____

_____

_____

___/___/___ Today I am grateful for:

_____

_____

_____

___/___/___ Today I am grateful for:

_____

_____

_____

___/___/___ Today I am grateful for:

_____

_____

_____

Kindness takes Courage

"La gratitud puede transformar los días comunes en días de gracias, convertir los trabajos rutinarios en alegría y cambiar las oportunidades ordinarias en bendiciones." –William Arthur Ward

__/__/__ Today I am grateful for:

_____

_____

_____

__/__/__ Today I am grateful for:

_____

_____

_____

Self-care I practiced this week / Cuidado personal que apliqué esta semana:

_____

_____

_____

_____

_____

One thing I am looking forward to / Una cosa que me emociona:

_____

_____

Leave any worries here / Deja cualquier preocupación aquí:

_____

_____

_____

La amabilidad requiere valor

● ●

"When life is sweet, say thank you and celebrate.
When life is bitter, say thank you and grow." -Shauna Niequist

___/___/___ Today I am grateful for/Hoy estoy agradecido por:

_____

_____

_____

___/___/___ Today I am grateful for:

_____

_____

_____

___/___/___ Today I am grateful for:

_____

_____

_____

___/___/___ Today I am grateful for:

_____

_____

_____

___/___/___ Today I am grateful for:

_____

_____

_____

Kindness takes Courage

"Cuando la vida es dulce, da las gracias y celebra. Cuando la vida es amarga, decir gracias y crecer." -Shauna Niequist

___/___/___ Today I am grateful for:

_____

_____

_____

___/___/___ Today I am grateful for:

_____

_____

_____

Self-care I practiced this week / Cuidado personal que apliqué esta semana:

_____

_____

_____

_____

_____

One thing I am looking forward to / Una cosa que me emociona:

_____

_____

Leave any worries here / Deja cualquier preocupación aquí:

_____

_____

_____

La amabilidad requiere valor

• • • •• • • • • • • • • • • • • • • • • • • •• • • • •

"Be thankful when you don't know something for it gives you an opportunity to learn." -Unknown

___/___/___ Today I am grateful for/Hoy estoy agradecido por:

_____

_____

_____

___/___/___ Today I am grateful for:

_____

_____

_____

___/___/___ Today I am grateful for:

_____

_____

_____

___/___/___ Today I am grateful for:

_____

_____

_____

___/___/___ Today I am grateful for:

_____

_____

_____

Kindness takes Courage

"Sé agradecido cuando no sepas algo porque te da la oportunidad de aprender." -Desconocido

_/_/_ Today I am grateful for:

_____

_____

_____

_/_/_ Today I am grateful for:

_____

_____

_____

Self-care I practiced this week / Cuidado personal que apliqué esta semana:

_____

_____

_____

_____

_____

One thing I am looking forward to / Una cosa que me emociona:

_____

_____

Leave any worries here / Deja cualquier preocupación aquí:

_____

_____

_____

La amabilidad requiere valor

"Wear gratitude like a cloak, and it will fill every corner of your life."
-Rumi

___/___/___ Today I am grateful for/Hoy estoy agradecido por:

_____

_____

_____

___/___/___ Today I am grateful for:

_____

_____

_____

___/___/___ Today I am grateful for:

_____

_____

_____

___/___/___ Today I am grateful for:

_____

_____

_____

___/___/___ Today I am grateful for:

_____

_____

_____

Kindness takes Courage

___/___/___ Today I am grateful for:

_____
_____
_____

___/___/___ Today I am grateful for:

_____
_____
_____

Self-care I practiced this week / Cuidado personal que apliqué esta semana:

_____
_____
_____
_____
_____

One thing I am looking forward to / Una cosa que me emociona:

_____
_____

Leave any worries here / Deja cualquier preocupación aquí:

_____
_____
_____

La amabilidad requiere valor

● ●

To Live a Creative Life We Must Lose Our Fear Of Being Wrong

-Joseph Chilton Pearce

"Para vivir una vida creativa debemos perder el miedo a equivocarnos"
-Joseph Chilton Pearce

"Attention is the beginning of devotion." -Mary Oliver

___/___/___ Today I am grateful for/Hoy estoy agradecido por:

_____

_____

_____

___/___/___ Today I am grateful for:

_____

_____

_____

___/___/___ Today I am grateful for:

_____

_____

_____

___/___/___ Today I am grateful for:

_____

_____

_____

___/___/___ Today I am grateful for:

_____

_____

_____

Kindness takes Courage

___/___/___   Today I am grateful for:

_____

_____

_____

___/___/___   Today I am grateful for:

_____

_____

_____

Self-care I practiced this week / Cuidado personal que apliqué esta semana:

_____

_____

_____

_____

_____

One thing I am looking forward to / Una cosa que me emociona:

_____

_____

Leave any worries here / Deja cualquier preocupación aquí:

_____

_____

_____

La amabilidad requiere valor

"Gratitude, like faith is a muscle. The more you use it, the stronger it grows." -Alan Cohen

___/___/___ Today I am grateful for/Hoy estoy agradecido por:

_____

_____

_____

___/___/___ Today I am grateful for:

_____

_____

_____

___/___/___ Today I am grateful for:

_____

_____

_____

___/___/___ Today I am grateful for:

_____

_____

_____

___/___/___ Today I am grateful for:

_____

_____

_____

Kindness takes Courage

"La gratitud, como la fe, es un músculo. Cuanto más lo usas, más fuerte crece." -Alan Cohen

___/___/___ Today I am grateful for:

_____

_____

_____

___/___/___ Today I am grateful for:

_____

_____

_____

Self-care I practiced this week / Cuidado personal que apliqué esta semana:

_____

_____

_____

_____

_____

One thing I am looking forward to / Una cosa que me emociona:

_____

_____

Leave any worries here / Deja cualquier preocupación aquí:

_____

_____

_____

La amabilidad requiere valor

"Not what we have but what we enjoy constitutes our abundance." -Epicurus

___/___/___ Today I am grateful for/Hoy estoy agradecido por:

_____

_____

_____

___/___/___ Today I am grateful for:

_____

_____

_____

___/___/___ Today I am grateful for:

_____

_____

_____

___/___/___ Today I am grateful for:

_____

_____

_____

___/___/___ Today I am grateful for:

_____

_____

_____

Kindness takes Courage

"No lo que tenemos sino lo que disfrutamos constituye nuestra abundancia." -Epicurus

___/___/___ Today I am grateful for:

_____

_____

_____

___/___/___ Today I am grateful for:

_____

_____

_____

Self-care I practiced this week / Cuidado personal que apliqué esta semana:

_____

_____

_____

_____

_____

One thing I am looking forward to / Una cosa que me emociona:

_____

_____

Leave any worries here / Deja cualquier preocupación aquí:

_____

_____

_____

La amabilidad requiere valor

I am thankful for my struggle because without it I wouldn't have stumbled across my strength." -Alex Elle

___/___/___ Today I am grateful for/Hoy estoy agradecido por:

_____

_____

_____

___/___/___ Today I am grateful for:

_____

_____

_____

___/___/___ Today I am grateful for:

_____

_____

_____

___/___/___ Today I am grateful for:

_____

_____

_____

___/___/___ Today I am grateful for:

_____

_____

_____

Kindness takes Courage

Estoy agradecido por mi lucha porque sin ella no había descubierto mi fuerza." -Alex Elle

__/__/____ Today I am grateful for:

_____

_____

_____

__/__/____ Today I am grateful for:

_____

_____

_____

Self-care I practiced this week / Cuidado personal que apliqué esta semana:

_____

_____

_____

_____

One thing I am looking forward to / Una cosa que me emociona:

_____

_____

Leave any worries here / Deja cualquier preocupación aquí:

_____

_____

_____

La amabilidad requiere valor

● ● ● • ● • ● • ● • ● • ● • ● • ● • ● • ● • ● ● • ● • ● • ● • ● • ● ●

¿Quién crees que eres?

WHO DO YOU think you are?

How you think about who
you are really matters

*Cómo piensas acerca de quién
eres realmente importa*

REFRAME YOUR THOUGHTS

We know that a regular affirmation practice actually changes the brain. Benefits such as decreasing health-deteriorating stress, increased learning performance, and positive mindset shifts are just a few known outcomes. The key to this is *practice*. Let's reframe some negative thoughts into a powerful affirmation specifically for you.

Para encontrar algunas afirmaciones poderosas solo para ti, reformulemos algunos pensamientos negativos en mensajes afirmativos positivos.

Negative thought
Pensamiento negativo ⟶ Positive affirmation
Pensamiento positivo

Change: "I am too sensitive"
"Soy demasiado sensible"

To: "I am Kind and Compassionate"
"Soy amable y compasivo"

Repite esto cuantas veces puedas! Repeat these as often as you can!

"When I started counting my blessings, my whole life turned around." -Willie Nelson

___/___/___ Today I am grateful for/Hoy estoy agradecido por:

_____

_____

_____

___/___/___ Today I am grateful for:

_____

_____

_____

___/___/___ Today I am grateful for:

_____

_____

_____

___/___/___ Today I am grateful for:

_____

_____

_____

___/___/___ Today I am grateful for:

_____

_____

_____

Kindness takes Courage

"Cuando comencé a contar mis bendiciónes toda mi vida cambio." -Willie Nelson

___/___/___ Today I am grateful for:

_____

_____

_____

___/___/___ Today I am grateful for:

_____

_____

_____

Self-care I practiced this week / Cuidado personal que apliqué esta semana:

_____

_____

_____

_____

_____

One thing I am looking forward to / Una cosa que me emociona:

_____

_____

Leave any worries here / Deja cualquier preocupación aquí:

_____

_____

_____

La amabilidad requiere valor

• • • •• • • ● • • • ● ● • • ● ● • ● • • • ● • • ●

"Piglet noticed that even though he had a very small heart, it could hold a rather large amount of gratitude." -A.A. Milne, Winnie-the-Pooh

___/___/___ Today I am grateful for|

_____

_____

_____

___/___/___ Today I am grateful for:

_____

_____

_____

___/___/___ Today I am grateful for:

_____

_____

_____

___/___/___ Today I am grateful for:

_____

_____

_____

___/___/___ Today I am grateful for:

_____

_____

_____

Kindness takes Courage

"Piglet notó que a pesar de que tenía un corazón muy pequeño, podía contener un gran cantidad de gratitud." -A.A. Milne, Winnie-the-Pooh

___/___/___ Today I am grateful for:

_____

_____

_____

___/___/___ Today I am grateful for:

_____

_____

_____

Self-care I practiced this week / Cuidado personal que apliqué esta semana:

_____

_____

_____

_____

_____

One thing I am looking forward to / Una cosa que me emociona:

_____

_____

Leave any worries here / Deja cualquier preocupación aquí:

_____

_____

_____

La amabilidad requiere valor

___/___/___ Today I am grateful for/Hoy estoy agradecido por:

_____

_____

_____

___/___/___ Today I am grateful for:

_____

_____

_____

___/___/___ Today I am grateful for:

_____

_____

_____

___/___/___ Today I am grateful for:

_____

_____

_____

___/___/___ Today I am grateful for:

_____

_____

_____

Kindness takes Courage

"Siempre da sin recordar y siempre recibe sin olvidar." -Brian Tracy

___/___/_____ Today I am grateful for:

_____

_____

_____

___/___/_____ Today I am grateful for:

_____

_____

_____

Self-care I practiced this week / Cuidado personal que apliqué esta semana:

_____

_____

_____

_____

_____

One thing I am looking forward to / Una cosa que me emociona:

_____

_____

Leave any worries here / Deja cualquier preocupación aquí:

_____

_____

_____

La amabilidad requiere valor

___/___/___ Today I am grateful for/Hoy estoy agradecido por:

_____

_____

_____

___/___/___ Today I am grateful for:

_____

_____

_____

___/___/___ Today I am grateful for:

_____

_____

_____

___/___/___ Today I am grateful for:

_____

_____

_____

___/___/___ Today I am grateful for:

_____

_____

_____

Kindness takes Courage

"Llena la tierra con tus cantos de agradecimiento." -Charles Spurgeon

___/___/___ Today I am grateful for:

_____

_____

_____

___/___/___ Today I am grateful for:

_____

_____

_____

Self-care I practiced this week / Cuidado personal que apliqué esta semana:

_____

_____

_____

_____

_____

One thing I am looking forward to / Una cosa que me emociona:

_____

_____

Leave any worries here / Deja cualquier preocupación aquí:

_____

_____

_____

La amabilidad requiere valor

• •

"A FRIEND IS ONE WHO OVERLOOKS YOUR BROKEN FENCE AND ADMIRES THE FLOWERS IN YOUR GARDEN"

-unknown

"Un amigo es aquel que ignora tu valla rota y admira las flores de tu jardín"
-desconocido

Llena tu copa

Fill your cup

With those that support your journey

Con aquellos que apoyan tu viaje

Fill this cup with the people that support you and your journey

Llena este copa con personas que te apoyen a ti y tu viaje

"Gratitude is not a passive response to something we have been given, gratitude arises from paying attention, from being awake in the presence of everything that lives with and without us." -David Whyte

___/___/___ Today I am grateful for/Hoy estoy agradecido por:

_____

_____

_____

___/___/___ Today I am grateful for:

_____

_____

_____

___/___/___ Today I am grateful for:

_____

_____

_____

___/___/___ Today I am grateful for:

_____

_____

_____

___/___/___ Today I am grateful for:

_____

_____

_____

Kindness takes Courage

"La gratitud no es una respuesta pasiva a algo que se nos ha dado, la gratitud surge de estar atentos, de estar despiertos ante la presencia de todo lo que vive con y sin nosotros." –David Whyte

___/___/___ Today I am grateful for:

_____

_____

_____

___/___/___ Today I am grateful for:

_____

_____

_____

Self-care I practiced this week / Cuidado personal que apliqué esta semana:

_____

_____

_____

_____

_____

One thing I am looking forward to / Una cosa que me emociona:

_____

_____

Leave any worries here / Deja cualquier preocupación aquí:

_____

_____

_____

La amabilidad requiere valor

"May I live this day compassionate of heart, clear in word, gracious in awareness, courageous in thought, generous in love." –John O'Donohue

___/___/___ Today I am grateful for/Hoy estoy agradecido por:

___/___/___ Today I am grateful for:

___/___/___ Today I am grateful for:

___/___/___ Today I am grateful for:

___/___/___ Today I am grateful for:

Kindness takes Courage

"Que viva este día compasivo de corazón, claro de palabra, amable de conciencia, valiente de pensamiento, generoso de amor." -John O'Donohue

__/__/__ Today I am grateful for:

_____

_____

_____

__/__/__ Today I am grateful for:

_____

_____

_____

Self-care I practiced this week / Cuidado personal que apliqué esta semana:

_____

_____

_____

_____

_____

One thing I am looking forward to / Una cosa que me emociona:

_____

_____

Leave any worries here / Deja cualquier preocupación aquí:

_____

_____

_____

La amabilidad requiere valor

• • • •• • • • • • • • • • • • • • • • • •• • • • • • • •

*"Count your blessings and you'll lose count of
your misfortunes."* –Jean Clervil

___/___/___ Today I am grateful for/Hoy estoy agradecido por:

_____

_____

_____

___/___/___ Today I am grateful for:

_____

_____

_____

___/___/___ Today I am grateful for:

_____

_____

_____

___/___/___ Today I am grateful for:

_____

_____

_____

___/___/___ Today I am grateful for:

_____

_____

_____

Kindness takes Courage

__/__/__ Today I am grateful for:

_____

_____

_____

__/__/__ Today I am grateful for:

_____

_____

_____

Self-care I practiced this week / Cuidado personal que apliqué esta semana:

_____

_____

_____

_____

_____

One thing I am looking forward to / Una cosa que me emociona:

_____

_____

Leave any worries here / Deja cualquier preocupación aquí:

_____

_____

_____

La amabilidad requiere valor

"May I meet this moment fully. May I meet it as a friend." -Sylvia Boorstein

___/___/___ Today I am grateful for/Hoy estoy agradecido por:

_____

_____

_____

___/___/___ Today I am grateful for:

_____

_____

_____

___/___/___ Today I am grateful for:

_____

_____

_____

___/___/___ Today I am grateful for:

_____

_____

_____

___/___/___ Today I am grateful for:

_____

_____

_____

Kindness takes Courage

"Que pueda enfrentar este momento plenamente. Que pueda enfrentarlo como un amigo." -Sylvia Boorstein

___/___/___ Today I am grateful for:

_____

_____

_____

___/___/___ Today I am grateful for:

_____

_____

_____

Self-care I practiced this week/Cuidado personal que apliqué esta semana:

_____

_____

_____

_____

_____

One thing I am looking forward to / Una cosa que me emociona:

_____

_____

Leave any worries here / Deja cualquier preocupación aquí:

_____

_____

_____

La amabilidad requiere valor

Notes:

Notas:

Notes:

Notas:

About Knowing You Matter
Knowing You Matter is a 501(c)(3) nonprofit organization that was formed from our founders'personal experience of loss, grief, and a deep need for healing after their son died by suicide. We aim to make a difference in people's lives through programs that promote emotional health and wellness. Our organization uses multiple levels of outreach to build a community of connectivity and support so that no individual needs to face their struggles alone. Our books are designed to provide positive affirmations that promote self-esteem and send an important message to every child that they matter.

For more information visit www.KnowingYouMatter.org

Thank you to our helpers/Gracias a nuestras ayudantes

Aleea Armijo, M.A.
It was an honor to translate this journal. I have a passion for bilingual and accessible tools for everyone! Check out @flashcards4dreamers on Instagram for more of my English/Spanish educational tools. -Aleea

A Peace of Werk publishes resources focused on providing children and parents tools and education that supports Mental Health to ultimately increase awareness, well-being and connection with ourselves and the people in our lives.

For more information and other resources, please visit: www.apeaceofwerk.com